When my daughter Emma was little I wrote special annuals for her, and also drew her lots of pictures to colour in. Sometimes I drew her characters from her favourite books, sometimes I invented my own. I drew Meg, Jo, Beth and Amy from *Little Women*, Katy from *What Katy Did*, and Pauline, Petrova and Posy from *Ballet Shoes*. I was so pleased that Emma liked the books that I'd loved as a child. I've written about *Ballet Shoes* in this annual.

⭐ ⭐ ⭐

It's at the forefront of my mind because Shirley, the girl in my story about evacuees in the Second World War, is passionate about *Ballet Shoes* and commandeers Pauline, Petrova and Posy as her special imaginary friends. I so enjoyed writing a story set in 1939. I wonder if you've learnt about evacuees at school? Maybe you're lucky enough to know an elderly person who was actually evacuated? I wonder how you'd have felt if you'd had to leave your home and be sent off to the safety of the countryside with just a small suitcase containing a change of clothes, washing things, a hairbrush, one toy and one book. Perhaps this book would be a good choice as it will keep you occupied for weeks.

Happy reading!

Love from

Flip over for lots of JW fun!

All About ME!

Name: ....

Age: ....

Birthday: ....

My hobbies:
....
....
....
....

Where I live:
....
....
....

Favourite book:
....
....
....

Favourite food:
....
....
....

Favourite colour:
....

Favourite music:
....
....
....

Favourite holiday:
....
....
....

4

My 2017!

My best memory of 2017:

What I'm most proud of doing in 2017:

....

....

....

....

The best book I read:

....

....

My resolutions for 2018 are:

My 2018!

Something I want to try in 2018:

....

....

....

Places I want to visit this year:

....

....

A book I want to read this year:

....

....

....

My best outfit of 2017:

In 2018, this is my dream outfit:

Sketch the cutest animal you see in 2018 here!

Draw the prettiest flower you see in 2018 here!

10 things about me!

Fill the notebook with facts about you!

1. ....

2. ....

3. ....

4. ....

5. ....

6. ....

7. ....

8. ....

9. ....

10. ....

Emoji Ratings!

Colour in the emojis to rate your fave moments of the year!

My funniest moment of the year was...

....

Something that annoyed me was...

....

Something shocking that happened was...

....

Something that I loved was...

....

7

DESTINY

JANUARY

Notes:

....

....

....

Special dates:

....

....

★ LUCKY DAY: 23rd
★ SPARKLY GEM: Garnet
★ SPIRIT ANIMAL: Deer

FEBRUARY

Notes:

....

....

....

Special dates:

....

....

★ LUCKY DAY: 9th
★ SPARKLY GEM: Amethyst
★ SPIRIT ANIMAL: Dolphin

MARCH

Notes:

....

....

....

Special dates:

....

....

★ LUCKY DAY: 14th
★ SPARKLY GEM: Aquamarine
★ SPIRIT ANIMAL: Lamb

JULY

Notes:

....

....

....

Special dates:

....

....

★ LUCKY DAY: 26th
★ SPARKLY GEM: Ruby
★ SPIRIT ANIMAL: Lemur

AUGUST

Notes:

....

....

....

Special dates:

....

....

★ LUCKY DAY: 8th
★ SPARKLY GEM: Peridot
★ SPIRIT ANIMAL: Fox

SEPTEMBER

Notes:

....

....

....

Special dates:

....

....

★ LUCKY DAY: 29th
★ SPARKLY GEM: Sapphire
★ SPIRIT ANIMAL: Dog

DIARY!

Discover your lucky day, sparkly gem and spirit animal for every month!

APRIL

Notes:

....

....

....

Special dates:

....

....

★ LUCKY DAY: 20th

★ SPARKLY GEM: Diamond

★ SPIRIT ANIMAL: Tortoise

MAY

Notes:

....

....

....

Special dates:

....

....

★ LUCKY DAY: 4th

★ SPARKLY GEM: Emerald

★ SPIRIT ANIMAL: Pig

JUNE

Notes:

....

....

....

Special dates:

....

....

★ LUCKY DAY: 17th

★ SPARKLY GEM: Pearl

★ SPIRIT ANIMAL: Cat

OCTOBER

Notes:

....

....

....

Special dates:

....

....

★ LUCKY DAY: 9th

★ SPARKLY GEM: Opal

★ SPIRIT ANIMAL: Rabbit

NOVEMBER

Notes:

....

....

....

Special dates:

....

....

★ LUCKY DAY: 14th

★ SPARKLY GEM: Topaz

★ SPIRIT ANIMAL: Owl

DECEMBER

Notes:

....

....

....

Special dates:

....

....

★ LUCKY DAY: 23rd

★ SPARKLY GEM: Turquoise

★ SPIRIT ANIMAL: Penguin

Books I Want To Read

Jot the titles of the books you want to read here

Colour in the books as you read them!

Reading is Dreaming with open Eyes

Colour in to complete!

13

BFF FILE!

Can you take the friendship challenge?

My Best Friend is:

....

How We Met:

....
....
....

5 Things I ♥ About My Bestie!

1. ....
2. ....
3. ....
4. ....
5. ....

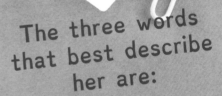

The three words that best describe her are:

....
....
....

Our best day ever was when:

....
....
....
....

Friend Fashion!

Choose a new look for your BFF by designing her a fab outfit!

Besties Forever!

Stick a picture of the two of you here!

Chum Challenge!

How much do you know about your BFF?

1. What colour are her eyes? No peeking!
2. Does she have a middle name?
3. What's her most embarrassing moment?
4. Which does she prefer — chocolate or jelly sweets?
5. Do you know what her favourite book, movie, TV show and song are?
6. What size shoe does she wear?

Now, let your bestie mark your answers — take one point for each one that's correct!

TOGETHER TIME!

Three or less

You don't know lots about your bestie, but that can be fixed by spending some quality time together! Arrange a sleepover or shopping day and spend a few hours getting to know each other better!

TWIN-TASTIC!

Four or More!

You're so close, you're practically sisters! You've put your friendship to the test and have a bestie bond that can't be beaten! Give her a treat and plan a fun day out to celebrate your chosen chum!

My Secret Invisible Ink!

Write a big **BOG OFF** sign on the front of your diary so everyone knows to keep their noses out!

You'll need:

* Paper
* Paint
* Paintbrush
* White crayon

What to do!

Write your secret messages in your diary with white crayon — no one will be able to tell what it says!

If you want to reveal your message, mix some paint with water and gently sweep it over the paper.

Let it dry and watch your message appear through the paint!

Diary!

Top Tips!

Mark out a time to write in your diary — there's no point having one if you never write in it!

Think about what to write — you can try filling in some information about yourself, like Tracy does. Write down your name, age, birthday, height and eye colour.

Some good hiding places for your top secret diary are inside a shoe box, in your sock drawer or underneath your pillow!

How to keep your diary super-secret!

MY DIARY

Try writing some secret messages here!

TRACY BEAKER'S
Spaghetti & Meatball Muffins!

Yum yum!

Fool your friends with these tasty treats!

You'll need:

- [ ] 225g plain flour
- [ ] 115g caster sugar
- [ ] 1 large egg, beaten
- [ ] 115g butter, melted
- [ ] 150ml whole milk
- [ ] Dr. Oetker Muffin Cases
- [ ] 10g Dr. Oetker Baking Powder
- [ ] 5ml Dr. Oetker Madagascan Vanilla Extract
- [ ] 100g bag Dr. Oetker White Chocolate Chips

To decorate:

- 100g Dr. Oetker Fine Cooks' Milk Chocolate
- 50g Toasted rice cereal like Rice Krispies, lightly crushed
- Dr. Oetker Easy Swirl Cupcake Icing, Vanilla
- 100g seedless raspberry or strawberry jam
- 2 squares Dr. Oetker White Fine Cooks' Chocolate (optional)
- Dr. Oetker White Designer Icing & Bright Writing Icing

Always ask an adult for help in the kitchen!

Before you start!

Preheat oven to 190°C (170°C fan assisted oven, 375°F, gas mark 5) and put muffin cases in a muffin tray.

TOP TIP! Use a cake pop baller to make perfectly round chocolate meatballs!

1. Sift the flour and baking powder into a mixing bowl and stir in the sugar. Make a well in the centre.

2. In a jug, mix the egg, melted butter, milk and vanilla extract together. Pour into the well. Add the chocolate chips and mix the ingredients together to make a thick batter.

3. Divide the mixture equally between the cases and smooth the tops. Bake for 22–25 minutes until risen and golden. Place on a wire rack to cool.

4. Break the milk chocolate into pieces and melt in the microwave in a heatproof bowl in ten second bursts. Stir in the cereal and allow to cool.

5. Form into ten balls and place on a tray lined with baking parchment. Chill for 30 minutes until set.

6. Meanwhile, pipe the tops of the muffins with easy swirl using the writing nozzle, making stringy piles of icing to resemble spaghetti.

7. Put the jam in a bowl and mix with a spoon to soften — add water if necessary. Grate the white chocolate using a fine cheese grater.

8. Place a crispy chocolate ball on top of each muffin and spoon over a little jam. Sprinkle with grated white chocolate to finish!

Dr. Oetker

Check out www.oetker.co.uk for more cool recipes!

18

THE DIARY OF ANNE FRANK

Meet the most famous diarist of all time!

WHO WAS ANNE FRANK?

WHY WAS ANNE FAMOUS?

Anne Frank was a young Jewish diarist who was born in Germany in 1929. She became known after her diary was discovered in a secret annexe of a house in Amsterdam, where she'd been hiding with her family during World War 2.

Anne's diary showed people how awful life was hiding from the Nazis and has inspired many who read about her courage and strength.

The Diary of ANNE FRANK

2'6

Anne Frank's diary was a red and white checked notebook — just like this!

Her diary entries talked about her struggles, her dreams and aspirations of being a writer and having her diary published as a novel — sadly she never got to see her diary become a hugely popular book, which has sold over 30 million copies.

Some tips on journaling!

Pick a special spot where you feel happy and comfortable to write and let all your feelings out on the page!

Keep it simple — don't go into it thinking you have to write 1,000 words. You can just jot down a couple of sentences about how you feel, or even draw a picture!

If you're finding it hard to think of anything to write, you could try starting a themed journal like writing down your dreams or writing about your favourite TV show.

A Day in the Life of Jackson!

This journal belongs to: Jackson

Imagine what he gets up to in a day!

Morning:

4am
That annoying fox visited the garden again — luckily, my barking scared him off! Success! Mum seemed a bit annoyed, though. She must not like foxes, either.

7am
Breakfast! Nom, nom, nom...

9am
A morning walk with my favourite person ever! Mum seems in much better spirits now. I had a lovely sniff round the park, following every new scent...

10am
Met my friend, Florence, at the park! We played catch and I got an excellent tummy rub from Florence's owner. Today's off to a good start!

Afternoon:

1pm
Think I'll take a post-lunch nap while Mum's writing her next amazing story. Perhaps she'll write about my adventures this time! I'd make a fab hero...

2pm
Ahhh, found the perfect spot to sunbathe in the back garden!

2.15pm
Got a ticking off from Mum for chewing the hand off one her precious Victorian dolls — oops! Feeling a bit glum now.

4pm
Jacob stole my spot! Thought about chasing him off, but he gave me 'a look'. I let him keep it, because I'm so nice — and a teensy bit frightened.

4.30pm
Knew Mum couldn't stay mad at me forever! Cuddles and kisses — yaaay!

Evening:

5pm
Mum looked out some old photos of me as a puppy. Wasn't I tiny?

6pm
I ate all my veggies at dinner — they're my favourites!

7.30pm
Wonder what Jacob's up to? I think I'll go and annoy, er, find him...

8.30pm
Jacob and I are snuggled up next to Mum while she reads. I'm so sleepy.... must set my inner-alarm in case that fox comes back — Mum does depend on me so...

Night, night!

A Day in the Life of Your Pet!

You could follow them around and see what they get up to — or make it up from scratch!

Now it's your turn — imagine what your pet gets up to in a day!

Name: ....

Morning: ....

....

....

....

Afternoon: ....

....

....

....

Evening: ....

....

....

....

MY DIARY

Why not turn your pet's diary into a story!

SUPERHERO

Make a statement with these punchy pins!

You'll need:
- Different coloured felt
- Needle and thread
- Scissors

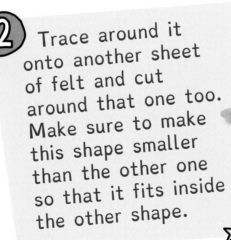

1 Cut a shape with jagged edges out of one colour of felt.

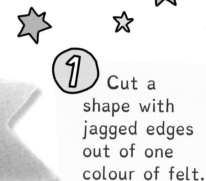

2 Trace around it onto another sheet of felt and cut around that one too. Make sure to make this shape smaller than the other one so that it fits inside the other shape.

22

SLOGANS!

3 Cut out letters for whatever slogan you want to use. We went with POW!

4 Stitch a loop on the back and add a hair grip or safety pin to use as a hair clip or badge.

Send us your pics!
jwmag@dcthomson.co.uk

23

My 2018 To Do List!

How many will you tick off?

Spring

Pick wildflowers. ☐

Dye Easter eggs. ☐

Bake a cake from scratch. ☐

Feed baby animals. ☐

Build a fairy garden! ☐

Invent a game and play with my besties! ☐

Visit three new places I've never been to. ☐

Take a selfie every day during 2018! ☐

Plant seeds and watch them grow. ☐

Add your own! ....

Summer

Throw a picnic party! ☐

Play frisbee! ☐

Camp in the back garden. ☐

Record a short film on my phone. ☐

Make an ice cream sundae! ☐

Stay up until midnight! ☐

Decorate an old pair of shoes! ☐

Collect seashells and make a collage. ☐

Go roller-skating. ☐

Add your own! ....

SKETCH BOOK

Make a summer scrap book. ☐

Autumn

- Take selfies in Halloween costumes. ☐
- Make homemade pizza faces! ☐
- Jump in a pile of leaves. ☐
- Watch fireworks. ☐
- Make leaf animals. ☐
- Watch a scary movie! ☐
- Go stargazing! ☐
- Stay overnight at a friend's house. ☐
- Carve a pumpkin. ☐

Add your own! ....

Winter

- Go sledging! ☐
- Have a pyjama party! ☐
- Make tree ornaments. ☐
- Knit a scarf. ☐
- Host a hot chocolate-tasting party! ☐
- Watch Christmas movies! ☐
- Decorate gingerbread men. ☐
- Make a winter bird feeder. ☐
- Finish two computer games. ☐
- Build a snowman. ☐

Add your own! ....

Read Or Write? ☆ Which will you choose?

Read a book about wild animals **OR** Write a story starring your family

Write a new Tracy Beaker story **OR** Read a book that makes you laugh

Read a book picked by your mate **OR** Write a poem about your bestie

Pick a song and re-write the lyrics **OR** Read a book set in a different country

Describe the messiest bedroom you can imagine **OR** Read a book out loud to someone else

Read a book — then act it out **OR** Write about a monkey wearing a red jacket

My Writing Secrets!

STORY SCHOOL JW JW JW

How to be a top writer!

I wonder if you think I drift around most of the day waiting for inspiration for my books? And then do you think I go into a wonderful book-lined study, sit at a beautiful antique desk, and start tapping on a state-of-the-art computer? Or do you think I sit with Jacob (my cat) on my lap and Jackson (my dog) at my feet, dictating to a willing secretary?

Wrong! Wrong again! And wrong a third time! I rarely experience that magic light bulb inspiration moment. But I still write every single day (even Christmas day!) whether I feel like it or not. It's the only way to get words on the screen. It might be a struggle to get started, but once I've been writing for five minutes I'm lost in my own story world and it's magical. I find it easiest to write first thing in the morning, perhaps because I'm only just awake and in a dreamy sort of state.

I don't go to a special study. I do have one, but it's a bit of a junk heap at the moment, with books and old manuscripts all over the floor. I nearly always write sitting up in bed in my pyjamas, with a cup of coffee beside me. I don't set myself an exact amount of words to write each day, but if I manage 1,000 words I'm pleased. I probably write many more thousands of words dealing with all my journalism, emails and letters.

Do you have a special place where you like to write?

28

I never thought I'd even get one book published. I can't believe I've now written over a hundred! I'm so pleased you enjoy reading them.

Beat Writer's Block!

Stuck with a story? My top five tips will have you scribbling in seconds!

1 I close my computer and take Jackson for a long walk in the park — and somehow everything sorts itself out in my head so that I can start tapping away as soon as I get home.

2 If I'm feeling tired and head-achey then I might curl up and take a half hour nap. I generally feel raring to go writing-wise when I wake up.

3 If I'm stuck writing a particularly awkward or difficult scene I might just sketch it out in three or four sentences and then carry on with the rest of the chapter. It's much easier to fill in the missing part later on.

4 It sometimes helps if I do something entirely different. If I go to the cinema and get lost in a film then I stop thinking about my imaginative world and return home feeling refreshed.

5 My final tip is to stop trying so hard. It doesn't always work sitting in a completely silent room. Try reading a book, listening to music or half-watching television. Chatter with your family. Write any old thing without thinking about it. You might find yourself writing rubbish at first — but with a bit of luck your imagination will take over once you've relaxed, and after a paragraph or so you'll be writing a super story.

Good luck!

10 Ways To Be A Great Mate!

Make your friendship extra-special!

1 Heard your fave song on the radio? Send your mate a text and rock out at the same time!

2 Pick them up a bar of their favourite chocolate, just to show you care!

3 Do they have a crush on a famous star? Pick them up a mag with the celeb's poster and slip it into their desk. They'll be thrilled!

Star!
Celebs, Celebs, Celebs
Super-Star Birthday Competition

4 Let them choose your next BF activity, even if it's something you don't really want to do.

5 Organise a sleepover and be ready with their fave snacks and a pile of their fave flicks to watch!

6 Support their newest hobby — if they need to run through lines for drama club, you're reporting for duty!

7 If they're having a bad day, think of something fun to do to cheer them up — they need a distraction, STAT!

8 Give them a great big bear hug the next time you see them — they deserves it!

9 Spot something in a shop you know she'd like? Get it for them!

10 Leave her a silly selfie guaranteed to make her smile!

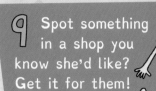

CHUM CHART

Be Friendly ☐
Be Trustworthy ☐
Be Honest ☐
Be Loyal ☐

I promise to be a brilliant bestie to: _____

Signed: _____

30

JW Bake Off Challenge!

Perfect your baking skills with our yummy recipes — or challenge your BF to a bake off!

Ready, steady, bake!

How to play:

- Pick a recipe each. You can do the same recipe if you want!

- Wash your hands and prepare your ingredients.

- Get baking! Once your bakes are finished and cooled, ask an adult or friend to rate your bake out of 10. The baker with the most points wins!

OR

Choose your favourite recipe and enjoy an afternoon of baking bliss! Ask an adult for a hand in the kitchen and whip up a tasty treat as a special surprise!

Beauty's Cookies!

YOU'LL NEED:
- 225g caster sugar
- 300g plain flour
- 200g unsalted butter
- 1 egg
- 150g chocolate chips
- 1tsp vanilla extract
- 1tsp baking powder
- A pinch of salt

Cookies + milk = yum!

1. Melt the butter and mix with the sugar in a bowl.
2. Sieve the flour, baking powder, vanilla and salt together. Add to the sugar and butter mixture. Stir in the chocolate chips.
3. Use your hands to mix until you get a dough. Then add the egg and knead through.
4. Grease a baking tray with butter. Take sections of dough, roll into balls and flatten slightly.
5. Lay them on the tray, leaving plenty of space between each ball as they will spread during baking.
6. Bake in the oven at 160°C for 10-20 minutes or until golden brown.

Tina's Lemon Loaf

YOU'LL NEED:
- 110g unsalted butter
- 170g self-raising flour
- 170g caster sugar
- 4tbsp milk
- 2 eggs
- Zest of 1 lemon
- Juice of 1 lemon
- 3tbsp icing sugar

So tasty with a cup of tea!

1. Line a loaf tin with greaseproof paper.
2. Beat the butter, flour, milk, sugar, eggs and the lemon zest until smooth and creamy. Pour the mixture into the tin.
3. Bake in the oven at 180°C for 40-50 minutes.
4. Pop the lemon juice in the microwave for 45 seconds and stir in the icing sugar. Pour the lemon drizzle over the top of the cake while it is still warm in the tin.

Tracy's Rockin' Road

Chunky choccy bites of heaven!

YOU'LL NEED:
- 125g unsalted butter
- 150g dark chocolate
- 150g milk chocolate
- 3tbsp golden syrup
- 100g digestive biscuits
- 100g mini marshmallows
- Chopped nuts or fruit if you like

1. Line a baking tray with greaseproof paper.

2. Heat the butter, chocolate and golden syrup over a low heat until melted and mix through.

3. Stir in the biscuits, marshmallows and any other filling you like. Pour the mixture into the tin and pop in the fridge to set for around 2 hours.

4. Cut into squares once cooled.

Sapphire's Fruit Scones

Enjoy with butter and jam!

YOU'LL NEED:
- 225g self-raising flour
- 50g unsalted butter (cold from the fridge)
- 25g caster sugar
- A pinch of salt
- 120ml milk
- 50g sultanas

1. Grease a baking tray.

2. Pour the flour and salt into a mixing bowl. Add the butter and rub the mixture together with your fingertips until it becomes like breadcrumbs.

3. Stir in the sugar and sultanas.

4. Add the milk and stir. Knead the mixture with your hands to make a dough.

5. Roll out the dough to around 2cm thick and use a cutter to cut out the scones. Pop on the baking tray and brush the tops with a little more milk.

6. Bake in the oven at 220°C for around 12–15 minutes or until golden and risen. Leave to cool on a cooling rack.

Superstar Songs!

Take our quick quiz and find out what you should write about today!

Director

Write a rockin' tune with Sunset and Destiny!

Movie Script

Tick the five statements that sound most like you!

You ❤ a power ballad! ☐

You can't wait for summer! ☐

All your fave songs are slow. ☐

You are always on the dance floor! ☐

Spring is your fave season! ☐

You love cold, crisp weather. ☐

You love writing stories! ☐

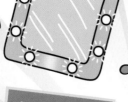

Your secret skill is drawing! ☐

Cheesy dance music, oh yeah! ☐

Violet from *Midnight* is your spirit friend. ☐

Elsa is LOL-tastic! ☐

You're feisty like Hetty! ☐

Mostly pink:

You are an imaginative and creative person, who would be suited to writing a ballad! Think of something (or someone!) you really love, and set about getting it all down on paper!

Mostly blue:

You're a deep and thoughtful person, who likes to rel-a-a-a-x. Think of a hard time you had and write about it, it's good to express yourself and song writing is the perfect platform!

Mostly purple:

You're a very happy-go-lucky person who loves to be silly and have fun! Write a happy upbeat tune — why not add some music or a beat? Make sure it's something you can rock out to!

1. Keep an ideas book and write down ideas as you go.

Still stuck for inspo? Why not take a look at some of Sunset and Destiny's top rock star tips?

2. Write about what you know — your pet, your friends or even your gran!

3. Songs don't need to rhyme, just fit with the beat!

4. Come up with a funky, catchy chorus, the rest will fall into place!

5. Practice makes perfect, put on a show with your BFF!

6. Don't be shy — rock out and have fun!

Now it's over to you! Got that song ready to rock?

Note it down here:

Jot down some ideas in a mind map if you get stuck!

MAKE YOUR OWN Fairy Garden!

Make your garden sparkle with these fun crafts!

Fairy Sparkle Jars!

You'll Need:

- Empty jars
- Glow-in-the-dark paint
- Paintbrush

What to do:

1 Make sure your jars are empty and clean. Dip your paintbrush in the glow-in-the-dark paint, making sure there's lots on the brush.

2 Put the paintbrush inside the jar and flick the paint around so lots of paint splatters get on the jar!

3 Wait until it's dark to decorate your garden or bedroom with your lovely new glow-in-the-dark jars!

Fairy Bench!

You'll Need:
- ♥ Wooden lolly sticks
- ♥ PVA glue
- ♥ Paintbrush

What to do:

1. Lay two lolly sticks upright, the width of a stick apart. Glue down three lolly sticks horizontally on top of them, so that you have the back of your bench.

2. Glue together four lolly sticks side-by-side. This is for the seat of the bench.

3. Glue the seat to the two vertical sticks and leave to dry overnight.

4. Once your bench is ready, glue on lots of sparkles and stick the two vertical sticks into your garden — ready for any tired fairies to come and take a seat!

Send us pics of your creations!
jwmag@dcthomson.co.uk

37

HOW TO DRAW BEST FRIENDS!

Learn how to draw Gemma and Alice!

SKETCH BOOK

1. Take a pencil and firstly sketch the outline of the girls' heads and necks, leaving small gaps at the top of Gemma's ears for her hair.

2. Draw lots of short lines to create Gemma's wild hair! Now add both girls' t-shirts, but leave a space on Alice's shoulder for Gemma's hand.

3. Fill in the girls' eyes, eyebrows, noses and big smiles! Draw a pretty flower on Alice's t-shirt and don't forget Gemma's hand on her shoulder. Add in their arms.

4. Time to colour! Gemma is wearing her trademark orange and blue t-shirt, while Alice rocks a more girlie look with her purple and blue combo!

Nick's Tip!

Use pink chalk to add a subtle blush to the girls' cheeks!

Sketch Gemma and Alice here – or draw yourself with your BFF!

All My Favourite Things

Making lists is so much fun!

My Favourite JW Books!

1. _____
2. _____
3. _____
4. _____
5. _____
6. _____
7. _____
8. _____
9. _____
10. _____

Places I Want To Go!

1. _____
2. _____
3. _____
4. _____
5. _____
6. _____
7. _____
8. _____
9. _____
10. _____

Doodle Box

Fill this space with lots of doodles — draw whatever you want! Here are some ideas...

Try Drawing These Things!

★ Things you love the smell of!

★ Your portrait!

★ Things that bring you joy!

My Favourite Words!

1. _____
2. _____
3. _____
4. _____
5. _____
6. _____
7. _____
8. _____
9. _____
10. _____

My Quote Wall!

Fill in the space with your favourite quotes from JW books! We've started it off for you...

Plug in your headphones and listen to your favourite songs!

Buy yourself some beautiful flowers!

Skip to pages 64–65 to LOL with Elsa!

Things to do when you feel sad ...

Write down why you feel sad in your diary!

Cheer yourself up by drawing some pictures!

Call your best friend for a quick chat!

Put your favourite stickers here!

My Favourite Songs!

1. _____
2. _____
3. _____
4. _____
5. _____
6. _____
7. _____
8. _____
9. _____
10. _____

My Birthday Present Wish List

1. _____
2. _____
3. _____
4. _____
5. _____
6. _____
7. _____
8. _____
9. _____
10. _____

My Fave Lines From JW Books

1. _____
2. _____
3. _____
4. _____
5. _____
6. _____
7. _____
8. _____
9. _____
10. _____

Stick a picture of yourself here!

Fill this space with your favourite words — using the hand you don't usually write with!

43

Pretty Posies!

Learn how to make these pretty pressed flowers with Hetty!

You'll need:
* Fresh flowers
* Tissue paper
* Cardboard
* Flower press (or some heavy JW books!)
* Patience!

1 Pick a flower from the garden, park or vase in your house. Make sure the stem is short, and remember to ask an adult first!

2 Open up your flower press, and make sure you have a piece of cardboard at the bottom.

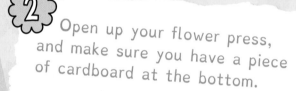

3 Place a piece of tissue paper down and put the flower on top.

4 Place another piece of tissue paper on top.

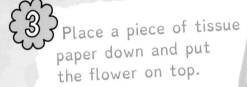

5 Pop the top of your flower press back on and twist on the screws to pack the flower in nice and tight.

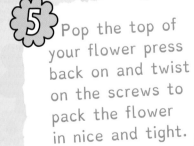

Leave for two days, and then replace the tissue. Leave for another few days to press!

Your patience has paid off — you now have a pretty pressed Hetty Feather posie!

1 Just like the flower press, place some tissue paper inside the book and then your flower.

Don't worry if you don't have a flower press, you can use your trusty JW hardbacks instead!

2 Place some more tissue paper on top and close the book over. Pop some more JW hardbacks on top for extra pressure!

3 Leave to press for a few days, replace tissue paper, then leave to press again.

Jacqueline Wilson

HETTY FEATHER

ILLUSTRATED BY NICK SHARRATT

Will Hetty ever find her true home?

Why not tape down your pressed flowers here and keep them forever?

Jacky's Favourite

Find out all about Ballet Shoes!

I love *Ballet Shoes* by Noel Streatfeild because it's a very realistic engrossing story about three adoptive sisters who go to stage school. The sisters are described so powerfully that they seem like your real friends. There are all sorts of fascinating details about what it's really like to go to a stage school.

Would you like to go to a stage school?
Yes, definitely ☐
Not really ☐

It's hard to choose my favourite character because I like all three girls so much. I also have a very soft spot for poor plain Winifred, who's very talented but never gets chosen for the best stage parts.

I think I'm probably most like Pauline who wants to act, but she does tend to be a bit bossy sometimes and order people about. I hope I'm not like that! Petrova is probably the nicest sister, and she's interesting because she hates ballet and wants to be a car mechanic. Posy is the most talented, but can be rather a show off.

Which of the sisters do YOU sound most like?
Pauline ☐ Petrova ☐
Posy ☐

e Book!

My favourite scene is when Petrova gets influenza and makes friends with Mr Simpson, who says she can come and help out at his garage. It's such a comfort for her to find someone who understands and couldn't care less that she's no good at ballet or acting.

What do you want to be when you grow up?

....

Super Secret!

I don't think I'd change a word of *Ballet Shoes* — it's perfect as it is.

I've read *Ballet Shoes* at least ten or twelve times, maybe more.

The book has shown me how hard you have to work to achieve any kind of fame!

I think the last sentence of *Ballet Shoes* is marvellous. 'I wonder' — Petrova looked up — 'if other girls had to be one of us, which of us they'd choose to be?'

My Favourite Book!

Fill in the details for YOUR all-time top read!

My fave book is: ....

....

I ♥ this book because: ....

....

....

Character I like: ....

....

Character I dislike: ....

....

Best bit of the book: ....

....

....

The ending was:

Amazing! I wouldn't change a thing. ☐

Wow! Such a cliffhanger! ☐

Hmmm, I thought it would have ended differently. ☐

Colour the stars to rate the book out of five!

I rate this book:

☆ ☆ ☆ ☆ ☆

Draw your favourite book cover here — or design a brand new cover!

Who Are You?

Which of **Jacky's** characters are you most like? Take our quiz and find out!

START

I love pink and sparkles!
— YES → **I love being the centre of attention!**
— NO ↓

I love being the centre of attention!
— YES → **I have a fiery temper sometimes.**
— NO ↓

I have a fiery temper sometimes.
— YES → **I prefer the countryside to the city.**
— NO ↓

I speak my mind no matter who I'm talking to.
— YES → **I prefer the countryside to the city.**
— NO ↓

I prefer the countryside to the city.
— YES → **I keep a level head no matter what!**
— NO ↓

I love to be the boss!
— YES → **I'm great at gymnastics!**
— NO ↓

I keep a level head no matter what!
— YES ↓

I'm very responsible.
— NO → **I'm great at gymnastics!**
— YES ↓

I'm great at gymnastics!
— NO ↓
— YES ↓

You're CLOVER MOON!

You are a kind and caring spirit just like Clover Moon! You're always looking after your friends and ask lots of questions. You keep your cool, even when you're solving tricky problems! You would make an excellent nursemaid to Mr River's children!

You're HETTY FEATHER!

You have a feisty personality just like Hetty Feather! You might lose your temper sometimes, but you always do what is right and look after those you love! You would rule the Foundling Hospital too!

You're DIAMOND!

You love the limelight just like Diamond! You have a show-stopping personality and love all things glitz and glam! Plus, Diamond's sparkly tiara and fairy wings would suit you really well!

Summer Story Starters!

Pick a prompt and get writing right now!

What to do:

Cut out the story prompts, fold them in half and pop them in a bowl. Pick one out at random and start scribbling!

Write a fantastical tale about a magical forest, a mischievous wood nymph, two gossiping fairies and a forgetful unicorn on a quest to end an evil curse!

You're emptying your suitcase when an envelope falls out. It says TOP SECRET in big red letters. What will you find inside — and who put it there?

KEEP OUT!

Gran's left her journal sitting on her beach towel and you sneak a peek at it. The very the first entry is dated 25/08/2253! Could Gran be a time-traveller?!

Write a story that starts: *The hot sun filtered through the window, but I couldn't help shivering, thinking of what had happened. If only we hadn't gone...*

You wake up on a beach with no memory of how you got there. There's a bottle glinting in the sun — could it hold the key to the mystery?

A summer fair has come to town with a very peculiar funhouse. Inside is a mirror that supposedly shows the viewer their future self! What will you see?

Why not?

Think up a title and design a front cover for your story!

My story is called: _____

My main character is called: _____

My story is set: _____

Guess Who!

1

- This JW character is partial to a chip butty.
- Her heart is torn between her home and the land down under...
- Life isn't always a funfair for her or her dad.

....

2

- This character and her mum would whip up a storm on the *Great British Bake Off*...
- Moving to the seaside sees a change in fortunes for her and her mum...
- Bunny cookie, anyone?

....

3

- Her dreams come true when she is gifted a pink bridesmaid dress.
- Her best friend Matty loves having her over after school!
- Can you hear wedding bells?

....

4

- This character is one half of *double* trouble!
- Unlike her twin, this character is bossy and likes to be in charge!
- Lights, camera, action! If only her twin hadn't messed up her chances of stardom...

....

5

- This JW character felt like a real princess when her dad gave her an emerald ring...
- Meeting her idol, author Jenna Williams, was a dream come true...
- A reindeer puppet kept her spirits up when she was feeling down!

....

6

- Working long days in the sweet factory can be exhausting!
- This is one outspoken heroine!
- She's all about girl power and is a proud member of the Suffragettes!

....

50

SPIN A POEM!

HOW TO PLAY:
- Pop a pencil in the centre of the wheel.
- Spin the pencil to pick a poem style.
- Spin again to pick a poem topic.
- Now write a poem based on your selections!

Write a poem with me!

ACROSTIC
The first letter in each line of your poem must spell out a word. For example:

Cute and cuddly
Always purring
That's my kitten

FREE VERSE
This is a poem with no set rhythm or length — and it doesn't have to rhyme, either! A free verse could go something like this:

The school bell tring-a-lings,
My heart soars,
Home, I cry!
   And onwards I go.

HAIKU
A poem made up of three lines and specific syllables, like this:

Line 1 — five syllables
How cold is the sea,

Line 2 — seven syllables
So deep and un-for-giv-ing

Line 3 — five syllables
The waves scare me so.

SCHOOL
FLYING
FRIENDS
LOVE
WITCH
STRAWBERRIES
BALLOON
MERMAID
TEARS

FIND FLOSS'S TICKET!

Oh no! I've lost my airline ticket to Australia! Can you solve all the puzzles to help me find it?

Friends & Foes!

Fit Floss's friends into the grid — the shaded boxes will reveal the name of her no.1 enemy!

Miss Davis

Tiger

Charlie

Billy the Chip

Ellarina

Susan

Old Ron

Rose

Put the 7th letter of this answer in the 2nd suitcase box.
Put the 4th letter of this answer in the 6th suitcase box.

Roll up, Roll up!

Floss has hooked a duck and won a prize! Cross out the letters that appear three times or more to reveal what she has won.

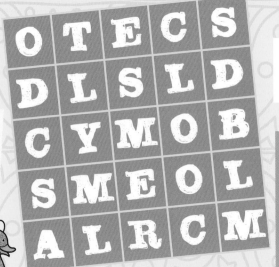

O	T	E	C	S
D	L	S	L	D
C	Y	M	O	B
S	M	E	O	L
A	L	R	C	M

The prize is a

_ _ _ _ _ _ _ _ _ _

Put the 2nd letter of this answer in the 8th suitcase box.

Put the 1st letter of the second word of this answer in the 1st suitcase box.

Charlie's Café!

Floss just loves her dad's famous chip butties! Solve the riddle to reveal a tasty topping for chips.

My **first** is in kettle but not in nettle,
My **second** is the third in chef.
My **third** is in try but not in fry,
My **fourth** is the first in café.
My **fifth** is in chip but not in clip,
My **sixth** is the last in menu.
My **last** is the final in fry up.

The topping is _ _ _ _ _ _ _

Put the 1st letter of this answer in the 4th suitcase box.
Put the 4th letter of this answer in the 5th suitcase box.

Fairground Fun

There's a new exciting ride at Rose's fair and Floss just can't wait to try it out!

BRAIDE__ELIGHT
SOL__PPOSITE
GRAN__RILL
EG__HOST
FRE__LEPHANT
FAR__ONEY
LES__YMPATHY

Fill in the missing letters on each line to make two new words – the mystery ride will appear in the boxes.

Put the 2nd letter of this answer in the 3rd suitcase box.
Put the 7th letter of this answer in the 7th suitcase box.

1 2 3 4 5 6 7 8

The lost ticket is on top of the _ _ _ _ _ _ _ _.

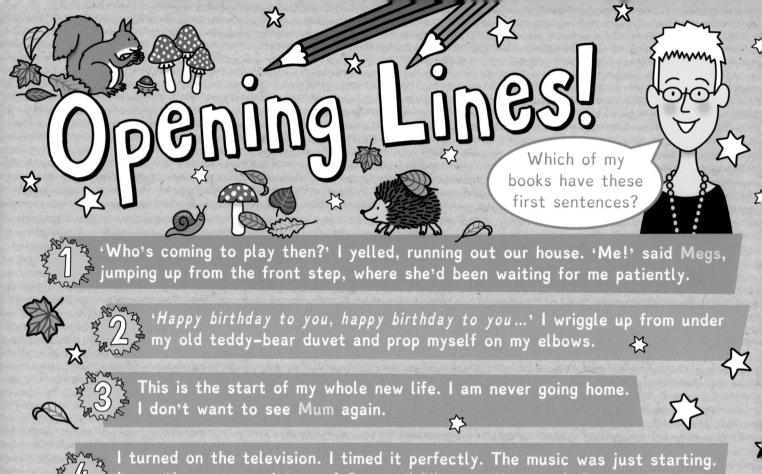

Opening Lines!

Which of my books have these first sentences?

1. 'Who's coming to play then?' I yelled, running out our house. 'Me!' said Megs, jumping up from the front step, where she'd been waiting for me patiently.

2. *'Happy birthday to you, happy birthday to you...'* I wriggle up from under my old teddy-bear duvet and prop myself on my elbows.

3. This is the start of my whole new life. I am never going home. I don't want to see Mum again.

4. I turned on the television. I timed it perfectly. The music was just starting. I saw the cartoon picture of Sam and Lily spinning round, Sam waving, Lily delicately nibbling a carrot.

5. Do you know what everyone calls me now? *Bed and Breakfast.* That's what all the kids yell after me in the playground. Even the teachers do it.

6. Let's begin with a happy ending. *I sit in the warm, waiting. I can't eat anything. My mouth is too dry to swallow properly.*

7. Alice and I are best friends. I've known her all my life. That is absolutely true. Our mums were in hospital at the same time when they were having us.

8. 'Guess what?' said Amy. 'It's my birthday next week and my mum says I can invite all my special friends for a sleepover party.'

9. When my parents split up they didn't know what to do with me. My mum wanted me to go and live with her. My dad wanted me to go and live with him.

10. You know that old film they always show on the telly at Christmas, *The Wizard of Oz*? I love it, especially the Wicked Witch of the West with her cackle and her green face and all her special flying monkeys.

Check how you've done here!

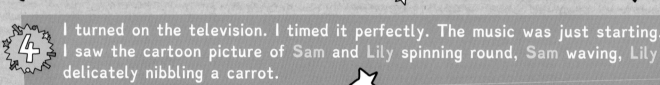

1. *Clover Moon*, 2. *Little Darlings*, 3. *Secrets*, 4. *Cookie*, 5. *The Bed and Breakfast Star*, 6. *Dustbin Baby*, 7. *Best Friends*, 8. *Sleepovers*, 9. *The Suitcase Kid*, 10. *The Dare Game*

PROMPT PICKER!

Speech bubble: Stuck for story ideas? Let the Destiny Decider choose for you!

WHAT TO DO: ● Pick a writing theme from one of the four corners. ● Count the letters in the word and open and close the Destiny Decider the same number of times. ● Now pick a number and open and close as you count out the number. ● Chose a final number and lift the flap to find your story prompt!

MAKE IT!

1. Cut out the Destiny Decider and turn it over so this side is face down. 2. Fold each

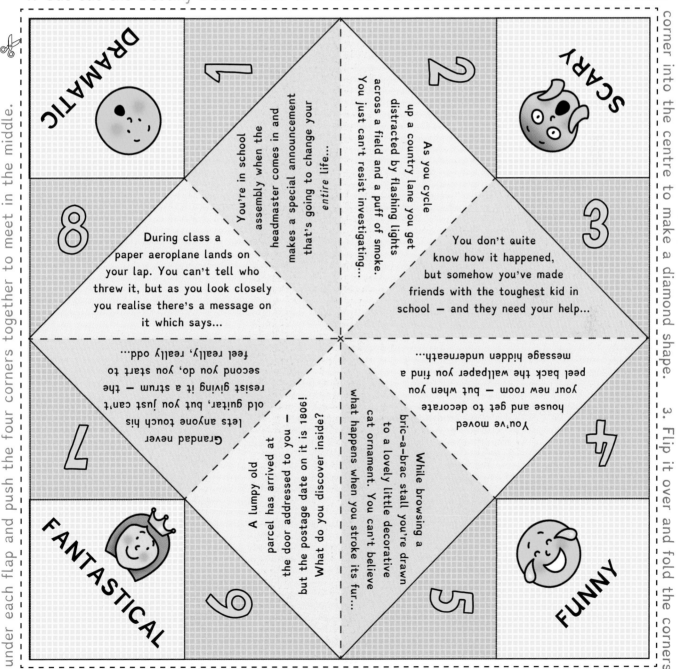

corner into the centre to make a diamond shape. 3. Flip it over and fold the corners into the middle again. 4. Fold the square in half. 5. Put your thumbs and forefingers under each flap and push the four corners together to meet in the middle.

DRAMATIC

SCARY

FANTASTICAL

FUNNY

1

2

3

4

5

6

7

8

You're in school when the headmaster comes in and makes a special announcement that's going to change your *entire* life....

As you cycle up a country lane you get distracted by flashing lights across a field and a puff of smoke. You just can't resist investigating....

During class a paper aeroplane lands on your lap. You can't tell who threw it, but as you look closely you realise there's a message on it which says...

You don't quite know how it happened, but somehow you've made friends with the toughest kid in school — and they need your help...

Grandad never lets anyone touch his old guitar, but you just can't resist giving it a strum — the second you do, you start to feel really, really odd....

A lumpy old parcel has arrived at the door addressed to you — but the postage date on it is 1806! What do you discover inside?

While browsing a bric-a-brac stall you're drawn to a lovely little decorative cat ornament. You can't believe what happens when you stroke its fur....

You've moved house and get to decorate your new room — but when you peel back the wallpaper you find a message hidden underneath...

School Quiz!

Answer the questions to find out what your next goal should be...

START

I'm a real go-getter! — NO → **Books are the best!**

YES → **I work best in a team.**

NO → **Ultra organised, that's me!**

YES (Books are the best!) → **I feel shy at school.**

I work best in a team.
- YES → **I get bored very easily.**
- NO → **Ultra organised, that's me!**

I get bored very easily.
- NO → **I love a challenge!**
- YES → **My homework is often late.**

Ultra organised, that's me!
- NO → **My report card wasn't the best...**
- YES → **My homework is often late.**

Books are the best!
- NO → **Ultra organised, that's me!**
- YES → **I feel shy at school.**

I feel shy at school.
- NO → **My report card wasn't the best...**
- YES → **I'm top of the class in lots of things.**

My report card wasn't the best...
- YES → **My homework is often late.**

I love a challenge!
- YES → **JOIN A CLUB!**
- NO → **My homework is often late.**

My homework is often late.
- NO → JOIN A CLUB!
- YES → MAKE A NEW FRIEND

I'm top of the class in lots of things.
- YES → MAKE A NEW FRIEND
- NO → TRY YOUR BEST

JOIN A CLUB!

You're strong-willed, dedicated and always looking to try something new, so why not sign up to a school group or team? All that's left to do is choose... will you join a sports team or dazzle in the drama club? Decisions, decisions!

MAKE A NEW FRIEND

You might already have heaps of friends, but there's no better feeling in the world than making a brand new bestie! If you're shy, then try breaking the ice with a smile. Feeling bold? Go on — reach out to a new classmate!

TRY YOUR BEST

Wave bye-bye to bad habits, say hello to success! Late assignments and sloppy writing are a thing of the past because you're super-determined to do your absolute best this year, no matter what it takes!

A+ REPORT CARD

My Summer Hols Story!

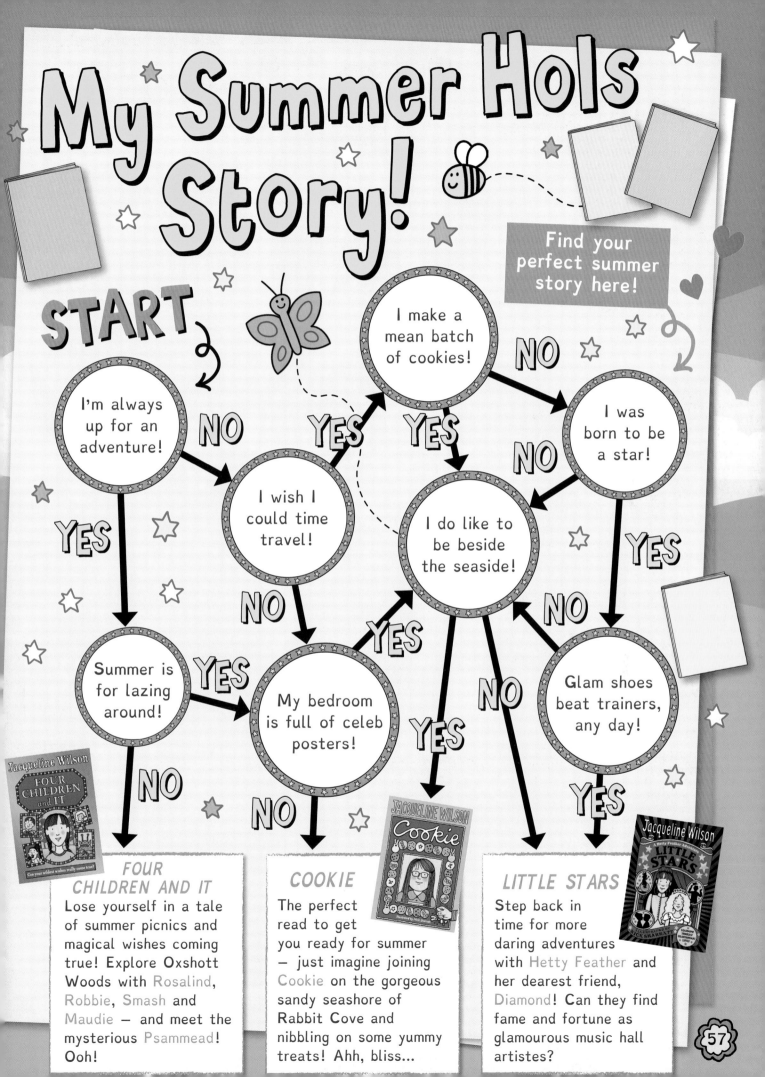

Find your perfect summer story here!

START

I'm always up for an adventure!

NO → I wish I could time travel!

YES ↓ Summer is for lazing around!

I make a mean batch of cookies!

NO → I was born to be a star!

YES YES → I do like to be beside the seaside!

NO ↓

Summer is for lazing around! **YES** → My bedroom is full of celeb posters!

NO ↓ **YES** → I do like to be beside the seaside!

I was born to be a star! **YES** → Glam shoes beat trainers, any day!

NO ↑

I do like to be beside the seaside! **NO** / **YES**

Glam shoes beat trainers, any day! **YES** ↓

FOUR CHILDREN AND IT
Lose yourself in a tale of summer picnics and magical wishes coming true! Explore Oxshott Woods with Rosalind, Robbie, Smash and Maudie — and meet the mysterious Psammead! Ooh!

COOKIE
The perfect read to get you ready for summer — just imagine joining Cookie on the gorgeous sandy seashore of Rabbit Cove and nibbling on some yummy treats! Ahh, bliss...

LITTLE STARS
Step back in time for more daring adventures with Hetty Feather and her dearest friend, Diamond! Can they find fame and fortune as glamourous music hall artistes?

57

Crafty Collage!

Design a cool collage cover for your journal or notebook!

You'll need:
- Cut-out pictures and text from old magazines (we used old issues of *JW Mag!*)
- Glue stick
- A notebook with a hard cover
- Coloured or patterned card

LOL

TOP Secret

1 Cover your notebook with the coloured card to create a background for your collage.

2 Arrange your cut-outs on the cover to get an idea of how they'll look. Once you're happy, start sticking them down to create your unique collage!

Cut these pictures out to add to your collage!

TOP SECRET

59

Over The Rainbow Cakes!

These colourful treats will brighten up your day!

You'll need:

- Cupcakes — shop-bought is fine
- Buttercream icing
- Blue food colouring
- Rainbow sour belts
- Piping bag

1 Bake your favourite flavour of cupcake and leave to cool, or buy some from the shop.

2 Put some of the plain vanilla icing to the side. Mix in a few drops of blue food colouring to the rest of the icing and ice the cupcakes.

3 Fill a piping bag with the remaining white icing and pipe two clouds on the side of each cupcake.

4 Snip a rainbow strip to size, bend into an arch shape and push each end into the icing clouds. Gorgeous!

Why not? Add some mini marshmallows to your clouds!

Ask an adult to help in the kitchen!

Brilliant Buttercream!

So easy — so delicious!

You'll need:

- 140g softened butter
- 280g icing sugar
- 1–2 tbsp milk

1 Beat the butter in a large bowl until soft. Add half the icing sugar and beat until smooth.

2 Add the rest of the icing sugar and one spoonful of milk and beat until creamy. Beat in a little more milk to loosen the mixture.

Rainbow Nail Art!

You'll Need:
- ☑ A variety of coloured nail polishes
- ☑ Sky blue nail polish
- ☑ White polish
- ☑ Clear polish
- ☑ Nail file
- ☑ Toothpick

These cute rainbow nails are so pretty!

What to do:

1. Start by painting all your nails in the blue polish for the sky.

2. Use the toothpick to draw on clouds using the white polish on every second nail.

3. Use the toothpick to draw on a rainbow on the remaining nails, with a little fluffy cloud at the bottom. Leave to dry and cover with clear polish to seal your design!

Our favourite Bad Girls quotes!

- ★ 'We were still best ever friends.'
- ★ 'That's why I want you to have it. My best thing for my best friend.'
- ★ 'Oh, Mandy. No one's ever given me such a lovely present.'
- ★ 'And then we had to say goodbye forever.'
- ★ 'We had to meet up again. Somewhere...'

LITTLE STARS

MINI PUZZLES!

Get puzzling with Diamond and Emerald!

Amazing Acrobats

Fit the words into the grid to reveal the full name of Diamond's gymnastic troupe!

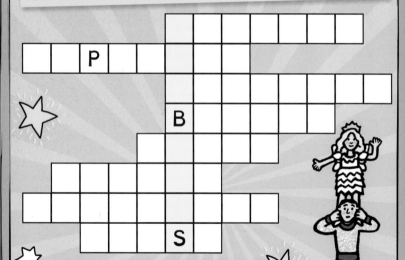

Monkey   Applause
Clown   Big Top
Magician Horse
Tightrope Trapeze

The Silver
....

Riddle Me This!

Solve the riddle to work out the name of Tanglefield's daring horseback rider!

My first is in BOAT
but not in BOOT,
My second is the
second of ODE.
My third is in PET
but not in PAT,
And my fourth is the
first in LAMP.
My fifth is in TIN
but not in TAN
And my sixth is
the first in NO.
My last is the
same as my third.

Madame ....

Sweet Snack!

Cross out the letters that appear three or more times to reveal a circus sweet treat!

C T R A Z M N D
T R M Y T F Z L
M O B R B S B S Z

....

Curtain Call!

Can you match these performers to their names?

A

B

C

1. Flora

2. Elijah

3. Mr Tanglefield

LOL-tastic

Brighten someone's day wi

These cards are sure to make your friends giggle!

You'll need:
- Coloured card
- Tea bag
- Googly eyes
- Glue
- Marker pen

1. Fold your card in half and glue on your tea bag half way down.

2. Draw on some facial features and glue on your googly eyes.

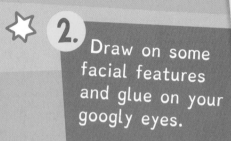

I think you've... TEA-RRIFIC!

Happy Birthday!!!

3. Now it's time for a pun! Tea-rrific! Geddit?

I think you've... TEA-RRIFIC!

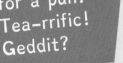

Happy Birthday!!!

4. Now add your special occasion message, decorate as you like, and hand out to your friends!

Cards!

...ese funny cards!

Make things all better and give this card to someone who needs some TLC!

How about giving this to a friend you just gotta 'ketchup' with?

We Must Ketchup!

Get Well Soon!!!

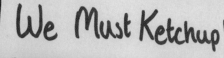

Hap-pea Birthday!

Make sure you give this to someone who will be pea-leased with it!

Why did the lazy man get a job in the bakery?

So he could loaf around!

What does a spider do on the computer?

Make a website!

Why was the broom late?

Because it over swept!

Why was the computer so cold?

It left the Windows open!

Snap A Story!

Take a photo every day of the month and use the picture to start a story!

Tick them off when you've done them!

1 A pair of shoes ☐

2 The weather ☐

3 An old book ☐

4 A cosy corner ☐

5 Something delicious ☐

6 Happiness ☐

7 Your favourite colour ☐

8 The view from your window ☐

9 Someone you love ☐

10 Your most prized possession ☐

11 Something close-up ☐

12 Your evening meal ☐

13 Your favourite socks ☐

14 Coloured pens, pencils or crayons ☐

15 An animal ☐

66

16 Something made of wood ☐

17 The sky ☐

18 Something noisy ☐

20 Where you live ☐

19 A spooky face ☐

21 The newest thing in your room ☐

22 Your favourite mug or cup ☐

23 An item that's black and white ☐

24 A circular object ☐

25 The last book you read ☐

26 Something pink ☐

27 A mess ☐

28 Nice and neat ☐

29 A smiley face ☐

30 Best friends ☐

31 A selfie ☐

For example...

Day one – a pair of shoes

- Who do the shoes belong to in the story?
- Where has your character been wearing them?
- Are they a comfy old pair that your character loves wearing? Or maybe they're a brand new pair that they're excited to wear for the first time?

Violet's Magic

Make some magic with Violet's spell generator!

Place a pencil in the middle of the board and spin!

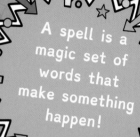

A spell is a magic set of words that make something happen!

Pick your element fairy! This will charge your spell with magic.

Fire: A spell for success!

Earth: A spell that will help nature!

Air: A spell for calmness!

Water: A spell for intelligence!

Happiness

Luck

Creativity

Love

Close your eyes and allow your pencil to fall on a flower to pick your magic words!

Lilac: Hocus Pocus!

Sweet Pea: Abracadabra!

Primrose: Alakazam!

Snowdrop: Shazam!

Now let's put tha together for some spellbinding magic

Combine your element fairy to power a spell tha you picked on the wheel. Remember to say your magic word at the end!

Spells!

Violet's spell uses the earth fairy, with a creativity element and the Sweet Pea magic word!

May the flowers in my garden,
Inspire me to be,
The greatest artist there ever was,
And ever, ever will be!
Abracadabra!

Protect things from mischievous fairies by sprinkling salt around them!

Fairies HATE silver.

Fairies love music!

Fairies love anything that sparkles!

Abracadabra!

Use this space to write your very own spell!

WOULD YOU RATHER...

Which of my dares would you rather do?

Only ever eat burger and chips **OR** only ever eat Smarties?

Stay at your current age forever **OR** be 100 for the rest of your life?

Never speak again **OR** blurt out everything you're ever thinking?

Sneeze cheese **OR** have tears made of milkshake?

Never be able to brush your hair again **OR** never be able to shower again?

70

Eat a pickled onion and jam sandwich **OR** drink a pickled onion and jam smoothie?

Spend a year living in a nursery **OR** a year living in jail?

Have a unicorn's horn **OR** a unicorn's tail?

Have a barky pet dog **OR** a scratchy pet cat?

Be stuck outdoors on the coldest day of the year **OR** be stuck indoors on the hottest day of the year?

Wear your grandma's clothes **OR** your little sister's clothes?

Never be able to watch YouTube again **OR** never be able to read again?

ARTY ANIMALS!

Happy Puppy!

1. Follow the picture to draw a puppy head with one big ear, a little triangle nose and curved lines for a smile.

2. Add a body with a short, waggy tail and two legs. Don't forget its collar!

3. Finish the collar and face, then add round spots in different sizes. Draw another two legs. Make sure to colour the spots a different shade so they stand out!

Stripy Kitty!

1. Sketch a round head with sharp, pointy ears. Give it a front paw, a line for its back and a long, curved tail.

2. Finish the kitty's body by adding in three more legs and a line for the tummy.

3. Give the kitty a happy face and colour in so it has stripes all over its body. Miaowvellous!

Fishy Friend!

1. Draw an oval body with two thick lips at one end and a gap at the other.

2. Give the fish a tail, then add in three square-shaped fins, as shown.

3. Add lines to the tail and fins, give it an eye and eyebrow and finish with a splash of colour!

Cheeky Parrot!

Sketch these perfect pets — they're so simple to do!

1. Sketch a domed head with a wavy line at the bottom. Add the top of the parrot's beak, a wing and a curved line for the breast.

2. Give it a leg and some tail feathers. Add the bottom part of the beak so it meets up with the top.

3. Sketch in another foot and two dots for eyes, then choose some bright shades and get colouring!

Beautiful Bunny!

1. Draw a rounded head and long bunny ears, then add a curved line for the bunny's back.

2. Draw in a back leg and two front paws with little squiggly toes at the end.

3. Add a round bunny tail and a happy, smiling face with big whiskers! Time for some colour!

My Dream Pet!

Have a go at sketching your own dream pet!

- Have you always wanted a fluffy kitty or a playful pup?
- Maybe an exotic pet, like a lemur or a giraffe?
- What about a mythical beast like a unicorn or centaur?
- How about creating your own animal from scratch — head of a lion, body of a snake, wings of an eagle? Sorted!

My dream pet is: ....
Its name is: ....
Personality: ....
....

73

Sleepover BFF Selector!

It's time to invite your friends to your sleepover, how do you let them know about it?

A With a glam, glittery invite! ☐

B By putting the details on sweet cupcake toppers! ☐

C Via a group text with lots of emojis! ☐

D You make invites that look like sleep masks! ☐

E You ask your friends at school — simple! ☐

What's your no.1 activity choice for your sleepover?

A Definitely makeovers! ☐

B A midnight feast! ☐

C Watching scary movies. ☐

D Camping out in a tent in the back garden. ☐

E Having a dance-off! ☐

Mostly As

You're a bit of a magpie and love anything glam and glittery — that's why you'd love to hang out with Amy at a sleepover! Just think of all the sweet 'n' sparkly fun you'd have getting glammed up and singing along to your favourite songs!

Mostly Bs

Bella

You have a bit of a sweet tooth and love baking sweet treats for your family and friends. Sounds like you'd have lots of fun with foodie Bella! From midnight feasts to the most delicious cakes and candy, her sleepover would be right up your street!

Mostly Cs

Chilled-out sleepovers are where it's at for you, and that's why you'd like a sleepover with Chloe best. You'd hang out, watch your favourite films and nibble on snacks like pizza and popcorn — just don't let Chloe put on a scary movie! Eek!

Amy

You need to plan a theme for your sleepover — what do you choose?

A A glam Hollywood party theme with music, makeovers and dressing up! ☐

B Pizza decorating, baking — basically anything food-related! ☐

C Themes aren't really your thing — you prefer going with the flow! ☐

D A fun theme where you can watch your fave silly YouTube vids and play LOL-tastic games! ☐

E A pamper party theme — you and your friends love to chill out together! ☐

Pick an emoji!

A ☐ **B** ☐ **C** ☐ **D** ☐ **E** ☐

Pick an object

A ☐ **B** ☐ **C** ☐ **D** ☐ **E** ☐

What would be the cringiest thing that could happen to you at your sleepover?

A Someone taking an embarrassing photo of you asleep! ☐

B Dropping an entire tray of midnight feast snacks in front of everyone! ☐

C Accidentally wetting yourself — oops! ☐

D Discovering you've mistakenly packed your little sister's PJs and have to wear them because you have nothing else! ☐

E A game of Truth Or Dare where your deepest secrets are revealed — eek! ☐

Mostly Ds

You're kind and caring, just like Daisy, and you love spending time giggling with your besties! A quirky sleepover party like Daisy's where you sleep out in a tent sounds like so much fun!

Daisy

Chloe

Mostly Es

You're super-active and love doing fun, energising things at your sleepovers — just like Emily! Having a dance-off or trying out home-made facemasks with all your friends would be your idea of fun — especially if you take lots of silly selfies together!

Emily

We ♥ Nature!

Make your own nature journal!

You'll Need:
* Cereal box
* Plain paper
* Patterned paper
* Button
* Needle and thread
* Small envelope
* Brown paper bag
* Glue
* Scissors
* Ruler
* Stuff to decorate

1 Cut the side from a cereal box. Measure out 26 x 18 cm and cut out to make a front cover. Fold it in half so the blank side is facing out.

2 Sew a button to the front cover. Leave around 50cm of thread hanging, so you can wrap it around the notebook to close it!

3 Open it up and glue a small envelope to the inside cover — you can use it to store things you find on your nature walks!

Trim a paper bag to size and glue to the back cover, making sure the open end faces out.

4 Cut some blank paper to fit inside the book. Fold in half and staple it in place along the spine.

5 Measure out some patterned paper to fit around the front. Glue in place. Decorate the cover however you like!

Over to you!

Head to a park, forest or your back garden for some nature spotting — and take a note of everything you see in your journal!

Take rubbings of leaves and stones or pick flowers to press.

Mark down the date and time, and a description of what you find.

Snap a photo or sketch what you see!

Do some research when you get home and jot down fun facts in your journal!

Things to look out for...

Nature Spots!

- ☐ Pretty flowers
- ☐ Singing birds
- ☐ Frogspawn
- ☐ Ladybirds
- ☐ Buzzing bumblebees
- ☐ Squirrels
- ☐ Leaves
- ☐ Fluttery butterflies
- ☐ Animal tracks

Wheely Wild!

Spin a pencil to find your nature activity!

Press pretty flowers that you find!

Feed the birds — they get super-hungry!

Hunt for animal tracks!

Use leaves, shells and twigs to make amazing pictures!

Sketch an outdoor scene!

Create a butterfly feeder for your garden!

DREAM BIG!

Fill in each list with the things you'd like to do!

5 Films I'd Like To Watch

POP CORN

3 People I'd Like To Meet

1 Outfit I'd Like To Own

Doodle it here!

4 Foods I'd Like To Try

78

6 Things I'd Like To Say I've Done

....
....
....
....
....
....

8 Books I'd Like To Read

....
....
....
....
....
....
....
....

I've written over 100 books!

7 Places I'd Like To Visit

....
....
....
....
....
....
....
....

PASSPORT

I've had two jobs — journalist and author!

2 Jobs I'd Like To Do

....
....

79

Jacky's Dream Journal

What do your dreams mean? Find out and note them down! Perhaps they will be the basis of your very first novel...

Flying

This dream means that you are spreading your wings and feeling super happy! But if you are struggling to fly in your dream, this could be a sign that something is holding you back...

Falling

Ever wake up with a start, as if you were falling? This is a sign that you are anxious about something! Write down anything that's bothering you, and make a pact to solve them, one by one.

Being Chased

Being chased in a dream isn't as scary as you may think! This kind of dream means that you are ready to face a big challenge!

Water

If you see water in your dream, this can be easily read! If the water is clear and calm, it's a sign that you are feeling clearheaded and calm too! If the water is stormy, this could be a sign of feeling confused or angry!

Teeth

A big toothy grin is a sign of confidence! If you dream that your teeth are falling out, this could be a sign of being nervous.

Food

Mmmm, food! If food appears in your dream, this could be a sign that you are hungry for success! You are ready to ace that test at school, win that part, or tackle that writer's block!

Jacky's Daydream

Daydreaming is sometimes the perfect way to think up a new plot, character or title! Jacky was struggling to think of Tracy's second name, when one day it came to her as she washed her hair with a beaker!

You could start a dream journal by keeping a note book next to your bed with a copy of these questions. Fill out a page after every dream!

Use this template to start your dream journal. Keep this annual next to your bed, and next time you wake up after a dream, scribble down some answers!

When did the dream take place? Past, present, future?

....

Who was in your dream? People you know, celebrities, strangers?

....

Jot down three main things that happened:

....

Was there anything different about the familiar parts of you dream? For example, — was your sister's hair a different colour?

....

Have you had this dream before?   YES ☐   NO ☐   MAYBE ☐

Is there something happening in your life that might have made you have the dream? ....

....

What does it mean?

Does your dream have anything mentioned on page 80 in it? If not, think about the people you met and what happened. Is something in your life making you happy, nervous or excited? Take notes as soon as you wake up for a few weeks. You may start to solve your puzzle, or perhaps think of a new plot for a book!

Destiny's Darling Ponytail!

This funky ponytail style is rockin'!

You'll need:
- ★ Hair bobble
- ★ Hair elastics
- ★ Hair brush
- ★ Hairspray

1 Comb your hair back into a low ponytail. Make sure to smooth down any flyaway hairs.

2 Tie a hair elastic a little further down from the bobble, and tease the hair in between to puff it out.

3 Twist the length of the pony tail through the teased hair and out from behind. You should be left with a twisty ponytail!

4 Repeat again as many times as it takes to the end of your ponytail and spritz with hairspray.

Ta-dah! The perfect look to rock out with your friends, just like Destiny!

Magic Memories!

Jazz up your journal with these arty tips!

Start with the title!

This is likely to be the biggest piece of text on the page, so make sure you give it plenty of space.

Next, text!

Add headers or memories — you can use your regular handwriting or even type these on the computer and print them.

Add big things!

If you have pictures or ticket stubs, do this next — that way you can fit wording and titles round them. Don't forget to add fancy borders to them, if you like!

Yummiest snack!

FAVE PIC!

MY fave OUTFIT:

Summer HOLIDAY

weather

M = ☀
T = ☁
W = ☂
T = ☀
F = ☀
S = ☁
S = ☀

BEST MOMENT:

When we went to the beach and Dad and I fished for crabs and he nearly fell in! I LOLLED so much!

AQUARIUM ONE CHILD ONE CHILD R2381 R2871

my best day out

I ♥ THIS!

Ditsy details!

Once you're finished with your journal page, add lots of little doodles to fill in the spaces!

Turn over to create your own journal page!

Awesome Inspiration!

Here are lots of different ways to make your journal look fab...

Practice drawing them in the spaces before you add them to your journal!

Borders and lines

Use these to make frames for things you stick in your journal or to separate sections.

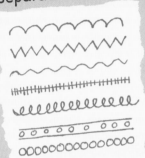

Arrows

Use these to point at important things!

Writing

Change up your writing to keep your journal looking interesting!

curly TALL
round POINTY
bubbly
messy! neat
old-fashioned

Titles

Try different title styles — you can draw these or cut out lots of letters from magazines!

TITLE
TITLE
title
title

Doodles

Use these to fill in gaps or add some interest to pages!

Write a Story with Me!

Let Jacky help you to pen your next adventure!

I promise this isn't like writing a story at school! I'm going to give you ideas, but you don't have to do anything you don't want to. You don't have to plan out your story first. You don't even have to finish your story if you get bored. This is all about writing for FUN!

I'll be the star of your story!

Let's make it easy for ourselves. We don't have to bother making up a new character. Let's go for one I've already invented. I'm hoping you might have read a *Hetty Feather* book, or seen the play, or watched the Hetty serial on CBBC.

Hetty is a small, spirited Victorian girl with bright red hair and a very determined character. She lives in a Foundling Hospital. However, if you don't particularly like writing historical stories you could always have Hetty living in modern times. I wonder what sort of clothes she'd wear now. It would be a treat for her not to wear that scratchy brown foundling dress. The Victorian Hetty likes reading and sewing. Do you think she'd have the same hobbies today?

Pick an era for your Hetty story to take place!

- [ ] Modern day
- [ ] Victorian
- [ ] Future
- [ ] Edwardian
- [ ] Medieval
- [ ] Wartime

Where will your Hetty live?

Country Cottage [ ]

Victorian Townhouse [ ]

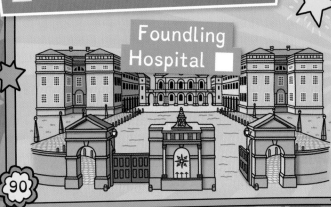
Foundling Hospital [ ]

Draw your Hetty here!

My Hetty's hobbies are:

Maybe you want Hetty to stay firmly in Victorian times. We can always change what happens in my stories. Sometimes they're very sad. How about writing a new story where Hetty and Ida live happily ever after?

I've made Hetty very ambitious in my books. She always loves to be the centre of attention and adores being the child-ringmaster in Tanglefield's Travelling Circus and performing as a Music Hall Star. But perhaps your Hetty might have different ideas...

I want my story to have a...

- [ ] Happy ending!
- [ ] Shocking cliffhanger!
- [ ] Sad finale!

Turn over to continue her story!

Do you think Hetty might want to work at the Foundling Hospital as she gets older, to try to improve the lives of all the children living there? Or perhaps she helps Miss Smith look after destitute girls in her special home? Do you think Hetty would always be gentle and understanding — or would she get impatient at times? How would she deal with a child as stubborn as herself?

What will your Hetty do with her life?

Will you include any of these characters in your tale?

Diamond ☐

Jem ☐

Bertie ☐

Madame Adeline ☐

Fantastic Freda ☐

Matron Pigface ☐

Let's pretend Hetty has actually taken over the Foundling Hospital. What new rules would she invent? Or would she want to abandon all rules and let the children do just as they please? That might be interesting!

What would happen if Hetty discovered Matron Pigface or Matron Bottomly were her true mother, not Ida at all? Terrible thought! How would Hetty cope?

Choose any one of these ideas and use your notes to get writing.

I'd love to see your stories!

You can send them to jwmag@dcthomson.co.uk

92

BFF Rainbow Necklaces!

Make these colourful necklaces for you and your friend!

You'll Need:

- Fuse picture beads
- Neck tie — we used a sequin lace!
- Parchment paper
- Peg board
- Thread

An adult will need to help you with this make!

1 Make two rainbow designs on your peg board like this.

2 Pop a piece of parchment paper over your designs, and ask an adult to iron them for 30 seconds in a circular movement.

3 Once cool, turn the pegboard upside down and peel it off. Put some more parchment paper over your design, and ask an adult to iron it again for 30 seconds.

4 String some thread through the top of the rainbow and knot it to create a loop.

5 Thread a neck tie through the loop and adjust it for you and your BFF's neck. We used a sequin thread, but you can use ribbon too!

Fabulous friendship necklaces for you and your BFF to keep forever!